KID'S CAMPING JOURNAL

 To:

From:

Because:

TO MY MOM,
WITH GRATITUDE FOR THE COUNTLESS COOLERS PACKED AND
LAUNDRY LOADS WASHED WHILE I PLAYED.

TO MY KIDS,
BECAUSE I WANT TO GIFT YOU THE SAME.

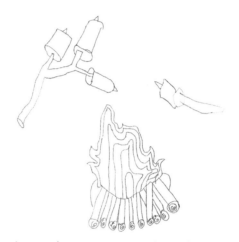

Art by Niklas (age 7) and Linden (age 3)

Flying Y LLC
PO Box 812
Livingston, MT 59047

Design and text by Katie Clemons.
Copyright ©2021 Flying Y LLC.
Published in the United States of America by Flying Y LLC.

https://katieclemons.com
Printed in USA

ISBN: 978-1-63336-048-8

I'M A HAPPY CAMPER

I squeezed my eyes shut. The morning air smelled like pine, dirt, and dew. Meadowlarks sang. A cool tingle of bug spray settled on my skin.

"Okay, all done," my mom said, setting down the spray bottle and plopping a sun hat onto my head before I bolted toward adventure.

There's something magical about camping as a kid. The world becomes your playground. Knees get scabbed. Adults and routines relax. Dirt decorates your campfire smoke-scented body. And somehow, burnt food tastes just right.

I loved camping as a kid, and I'm grateful that my family, like countless other campers, logged our adventures in journals. Wherever we went, our journals went. My mom encouraged my siblings and me to each log our unique memories and discoveries. Every trip, we sat at the picnic table or tucked our journals into our backpacks on day hikes. We recorded facts and told stories through words, drawings, and found objects. Sometimes we wrote a lot, other times we barely paused to jot a few notes. But she always made sure we kept journaling.

None of us could have imagined what incredible time capsules our logbooks would become.

A camping journal isn't just a record of place and time. It's a timepiece of adventure. It chronicles relationships with people you love and the nature you explore. Together. As you write, your journal becomes a treasure box, filled with the wonderful stories that you can't stop thinking about when you crawl into your sleeping bag at night.

Your journal is divided into four sections:

1. FUN GUiDED PROMPTS invite you to think broadly about camping and nature observations. You can use these pages during any trip or even at home. *Pages 5 to 35 and 96 to 100.*

2. COLOR AND CUT ACTiViTiES offer you the creative opportunity to play games and create projects. *Pages 36 to 44.*

3. A PROGRESS CHART FOR 25 CAMPiNG TRiPS helps you track how many camping trips you log. Each time you camp, color in a number. *Page 45.*

4. LOGBOOK PAGES FOR 25 CAMPiNG TRiPS enable you to record specific stories and discoveries of each trip you take. *Pages 46 to 95.*

Thanks for letting this journal and me join your journey. Write to me any time **howdy@katieclemons.com** (I answer all my mail), or tag me on social media **@katierclemons #katieclemonsjournals #myfirstjournals**.

Adventure awaits. Let's celebrate your story!

Katie

P.S. Enjoy the FREE exclusive printables and journaling games my family enjoys by visiting:

https://katieclemons.com/a/JNCT/

HELLO ADVENTURE

This camping log belongs to

I like people to call me

I'm age _____.

My home address is

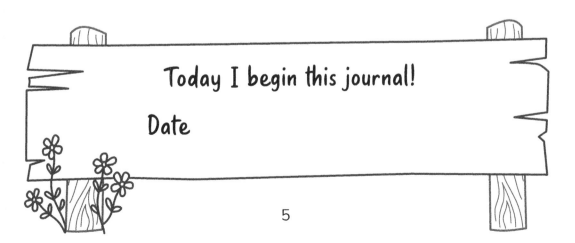

Today I begin this journal!

Date

MY JOURNAL GUIDELINES

Is my journal top secret or can anyone look inside?

If someone finds this journal, they should

☐ Return it

☐ Finish it

☐ Destroy it

☐ Drop it off at

_____

☐ Sell it for $ _____

☐ Email or text an adult with me at

_____

_____

_____

My top focuses in this journal will be to

☐ Record adventures

☐ Use perfect grammar

☐ Play on the pages

☐ Express my ideas

☐ _____

_____

Where should I keep my journal when I'm not using it?

Do I need to fill out the first section of my journal in numerical order?

☐ Yes   ☐ No

Do I want to log every camping trip I take?

☐ Yes   ☐ No

Will I leave my camp-sites cleaner than I found them?

☐ Yes   ☐ No

Any other guidelines I should establish?

FUN JOURNALING IDEAS TO TRY

The most creative journals are usually constructed with just a pencil or pen, maybe some tape, stickers, or colored pencils.

Here's the supplies I always want to keep with my journal:

Here are eight creative ways to record adventures.
Check off each one I try.

☐ **MAKE RUBBINGS.**
Use the side of a pencil or crayon to transpose an interesting texture onto the page. Try leaves, picnic tables and benches, or other interesting finds.

☐ **DRAW A COMIC.**
Add sound effects with fun words like BAM, TWEET, WOOF, and SCREEEEECH.

☐ **INVITE HELP.**
Ask someone on the trip to contribute to a page.

☐ **TRY A NATURE SKETCH.**
Tell wordless stories by drawing sights, sounds, and smells.

☐ **WRITE IN DIFFERENT DIRECTIONS.**
Rotate this book, then try journaling upside down or in a circle. Make words go up and down. Write backwards.

☐ **MAKE STICK FIGURES.**
Use simple shapes and lines to create people and animals.

☐ **CREATE A MAP.**
Use doodles, words, and arrows to chart one day.

☐ **ADD MEMORABILIA.**
Tuck in a postcard or brochure. Add a camp sticker or stamp. Tape on a campsite receipt.

Here's a drawing or photograph of me

I LOVE TO CAMP
BECAUSE...

ALL THE WAYS I'VE CAMPED

Color them in

In a backyard

Under the stars

In a hammock

In an igloo or snow cave

In a yurt or teepee

In a tree fort

In a van or camper van

In a boat

In a car

In a tent

In a camper or RV

In a cabin

In a _____

12

My favorite way to camp

The place where I probably camp the most

An adult in my group always says

A great camping trip usually includes

1.

2.

3.

I estimate the number of

Nights I've spent in a tent

Nights I've spent in a camper

The most mosquito bites I've gotten on one trip

Cans of bug spray we'll use this year

I LiKE CAMPiNG WiTH ALL OF YOU

Name _____

so fun

Name _____

♡ya

Name _____

14

If I were in charge of designing
MATCHING CAMP SHIRTS

15

THINGS I PACK

THiS iS ME WHEN

I climb out of my sleeping bag

I get woken by
_____

I explore the camp

I can't stop grinning

I eat a s'more

I write in this journal

17

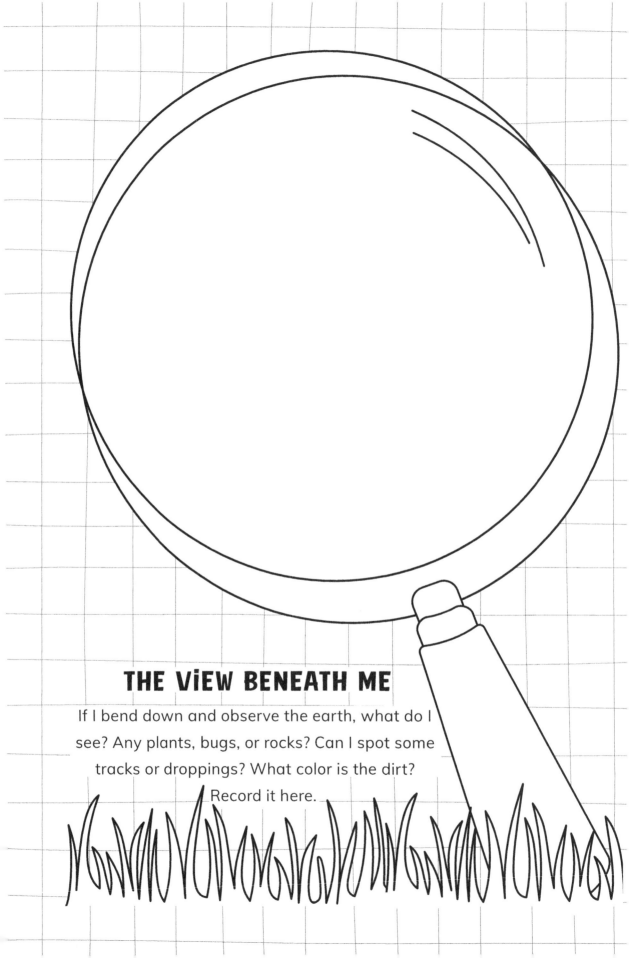

THE VIEW BENEATH ME

If I bend down and observe the earth, what do I see? Any plants, bugs, or rocks? Can I spot some tracks or droppings? What color is the dirt? Record it here.

I HAVE CAMPED

During these seasons

Winter

Spring

Summer

Autumn

Color them in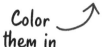

In this kind of weather

Intense heat

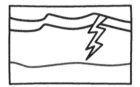
A thunder-storm

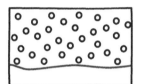
Hail or freezing rain

Strong wind

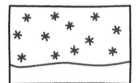
Snow

Rain

Fog

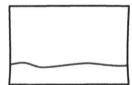
_____

Here's my favorite!

19

iF I RAN A CAMP STORE

Fill the shelves!

shop name

CANDY

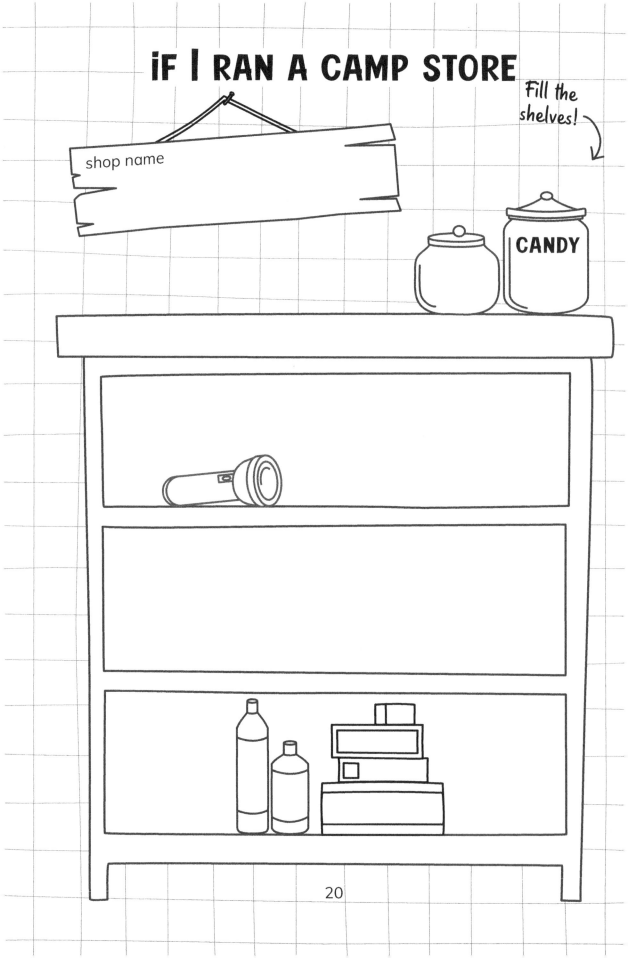

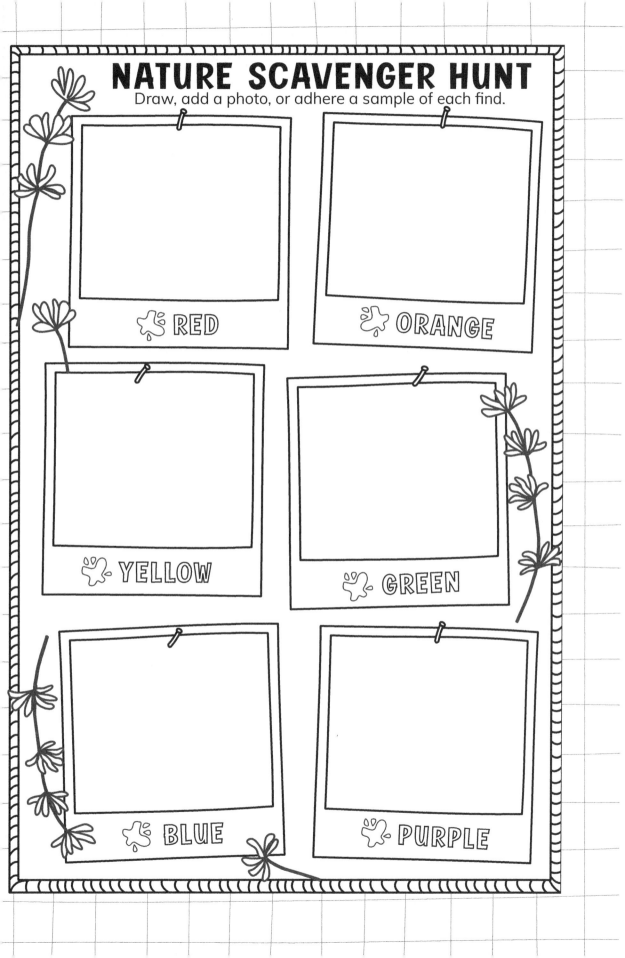

NATURE SCAVENGER HUNT
Draw, add a photo, or adhere a sample of each find.

RED

ORANGE

YELLOW

GREEN

BLUE

PURPLE

MY FAVORITE CAMP FOODS

Breakfast

Picnic lunch

Snack

Burnt but edible

Campfire food

Dessert

NATURE BINGO

at _____

How many things can I find today?
Draw each discovery, or color in the box. Can I get five in a row?

ant	spider-web	bee	big animal	frog
snake	animal tracks	nest	beetle	large bird
boulder	feather	FREE	fern	mosquito
squirrel	stump	moss	butterfly	mush-room
water	wild-flower	cactus	lizard	worm

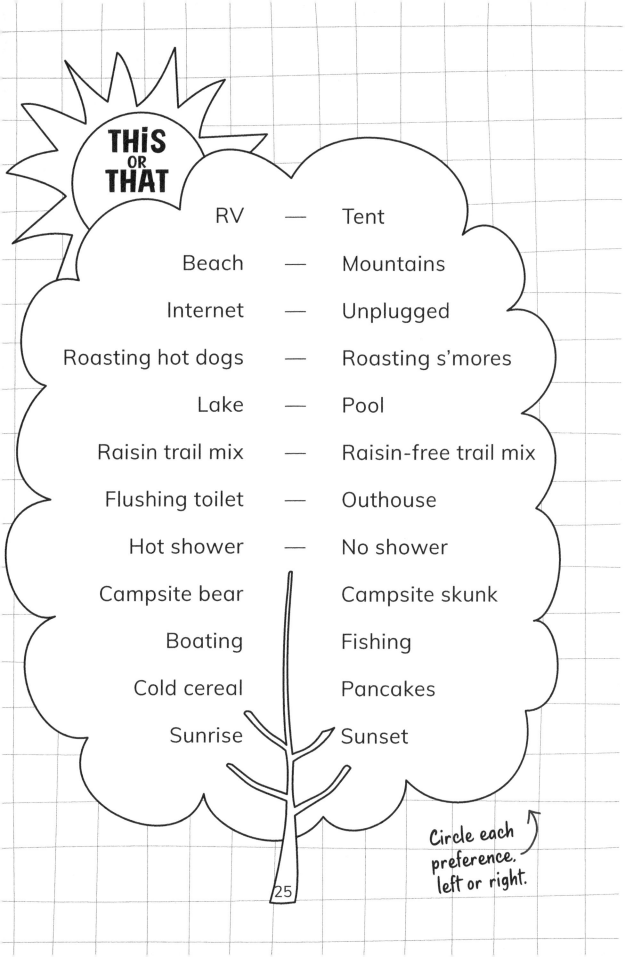

THIS OR THAT

RV	—	Tent
Beach	—	Mountains
Internet	—	Unplugged
Roasting hot dogs	—	Roasting s'mores
Lake	—	Pool
Raisin trail mix	—	Raisin-free trail mix
Flushing toilet	—	Outhouse
Hot shower	—	No shower
Campsite bear		Campsite skunk
Boating		Fishing
Cold cereal		Pancakes
Sunrise		Sunset

Circle each preference, left or right.

25

THiS MEMORY
MAKES ME LOL

THE VIEW ABOVE ME

If I lay down outside and observe the sky and plants above, what do I see? What do I hear? Any birds, bugs, or trees? What colors are the clouds? Record it here.

THIS IS ME WHEN

I drink a

_____

I forget my

_____

I spot an
animal

I can't stop
laughing

We arrive at the
campsite

I'm ready
to sleep

Today at

_____

I SPY

An animal that's
larger than me

An animal that's
tinier than me

A plant that's
taller than me

A plant that's
smaller than me

A bird making noise

An insect without wings

HOW TO DRAW

WHEN IT'S DARK OUT

AROUND THE FIRE WITH _____

ROASTING _____
ON THE FIRE

iF I iNVENTED A GREAT PLACE TO CAMP

Name

Area Map

Kids would
say my place is so

Nightly rate $_____

These are welcome
- ☐ Tents
- ☐ RVs
- ☐ Bikes
- ☐ Fishing
- ☐ Pets
- ☐ Campfires
- ☐ Generators
- ☐ _____

Today at _____ ,

I SPY SOMETHING

Above me

Bigger than me

The same size as me

Smaller than me

Below me

A place for doodles and daydreams

COLOR AND CUT
ACTIVITIES

The next pages are paper projects to color, cut, and use while camping.

Find more (free!) printables like these at
katieclemons.com/a/jnct/

Enjoy nature drawing tutorials and activities at
katieclemons.com/a/f1kt/

CAMPING JOKES

Cut out the squares and share some laughs.

---

1. What did the beaver say to the tree?

---

2. What's a tree's favorite drink?

---

3. Why do trees have so many friends?

---

4. What do bears call people in sleeping bags?

---

5. Why don't mummies camp?

---

6. Did you hear the joke about the skunk who went camping?

---

7. Where should you keep your money on a camping trip?

---

8. Why don't cows camp in cabins?

---

9. Where do sheep like to camp?

---

10. What do you call a bear with no teeth?

CAMPiNG JOKES - ANSWER KEY

2. Root beer.

1. "It's been nice gnawing you!"

4. Burritos.

3. They branch out.

6. Never mind. It stinks.

5. They're afraid to unwind.

9. They prefer sleeping under the mooooo-n.

7. In the riverbank.

10. A gummy bear.

9. In the baa-ckyard.

CAMPING CHARADES

Cut out the squares, put them in a bowl, and take turns drawing one. Act out the scene. Can anyone guess?

Spot a bear	Be a tourist	Catch a fish
Park an RV	Burn a marsh-mallow	Cross a creek
Catch a bug	Relax in a camp chair	Spot a hawk or eagle
Paddle a boat	Make a hot dog	Build a fire
Read a map	Go on a hike	Try to get cell service

41

BUILD A KEEPSAKE ENVELOPE

❶ Color and cut out, image facing down.

❷ Fold in side flaps. Glue or tape together.

❸ Fold in bottom flap and adhere.

❹ Fill then fold down top flap.

Tuck this pocket into your journal or adhere it to the inside cover. Fill it with fun finds.

MEMORIES THAT LAST

MY CAMPING LOG

The next 50 pages are for recording 25 camping trips.
Every time I log a trip, I also color in a number here.

How long will it take to fill the pages?

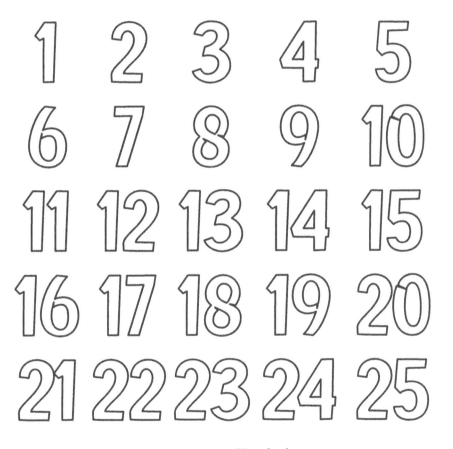

1 2 3 4 5
6 7 8 9 10
11 12 13 14 15
16 17 18 19 20
21 22 23 24 25

Start date _____ End date _____

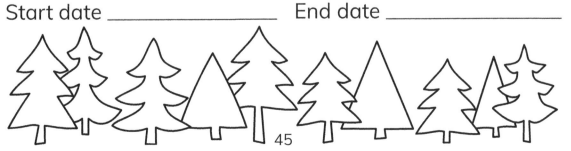

CAMPING TRIP 1

at _____

Dates

Overnights
1 2 3 4

Weather

Sleeping in a

I want to
remember this story

HERE'S THE SPOT

I see

I hear

I touch

I'M HERE WITH

LOL!

THIS IS SO

I LIKE / DON'T LIKE DOING THIS

I smell

I taste

I GIVE THE TRIP ☆☆☆☆☆ STARS!

CAMPING TRIP 2

at _____

Dates

Overnights

1 2 3 4

Weather

Sleeping in a

Glad I brought

HERE'S THE SPOT

I want to remember
this story

I'M HERE WITH

AROUND HERE

I see

I hear

I smell

I taste

I feel

THIS IS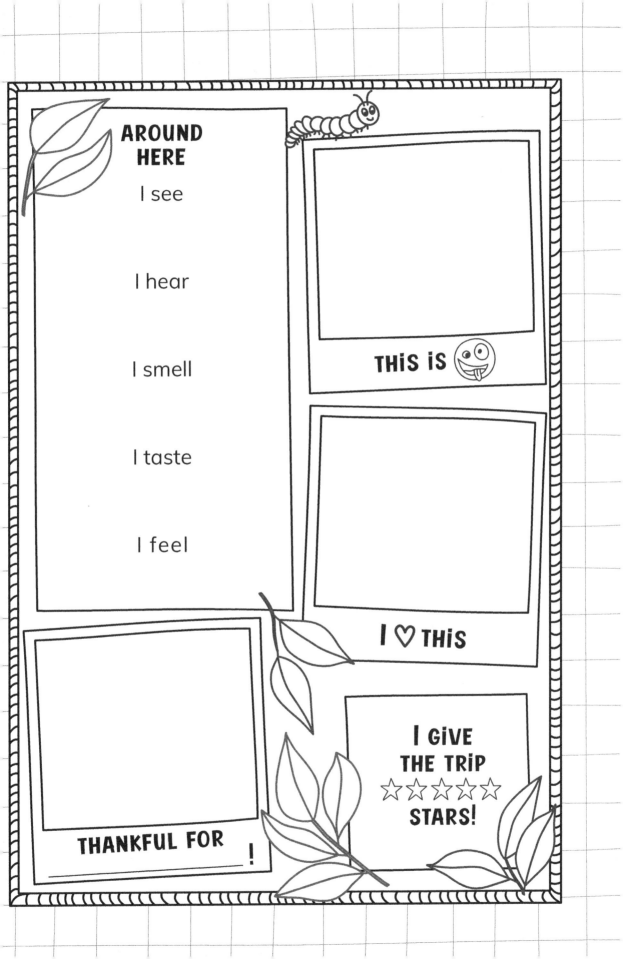

I ♡ THIS

THANKFUL FOR _____ !

I GIVE
THE TRIP
☆☆☆☆☆
STARS!

CAMPING TRIP 3

at _____

Dates

Overnights
1 2 3 4

Sleeping in a

Weather

I see

I hear

I taste

I smell

HERE'S THE SPOT

I'M HERE WITH

_____

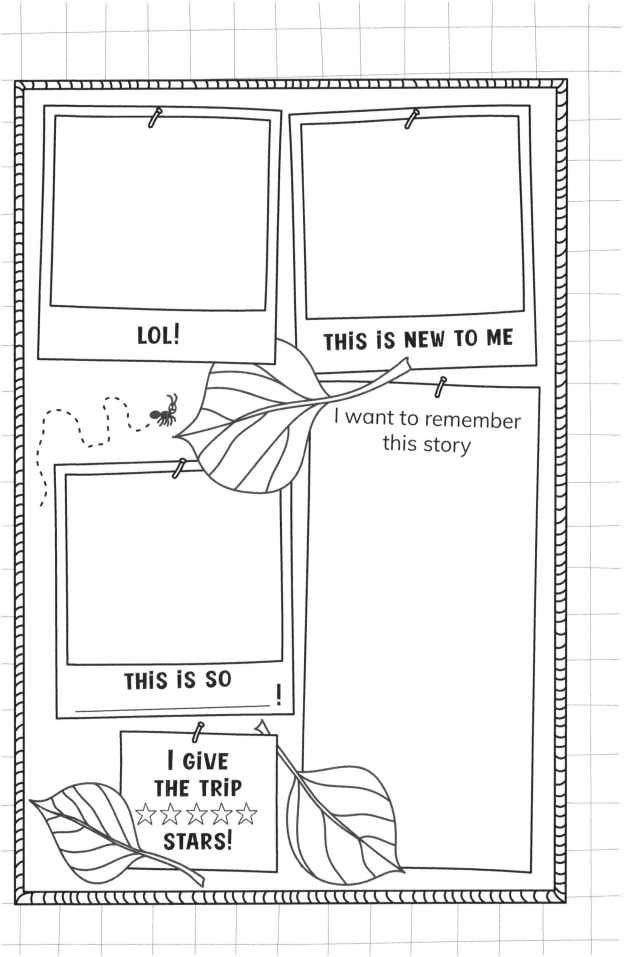

LOL!

THIS IS NEW TO ME

I want to remember this story

THIS IS SO _____!

I GIVE THE TRIP ☆☆☆☆☆ STARS!

CAMPING TRIP 4

at _____

Dates

Overnights
(1) (2) (3) (4) ( )

Weather

Sleeping in a

HERE'S THE SPOT

I want to remember
this story

I'M HERE WITH
_____

I see

I hear

I smell

I taste

I feel

I wonder

FIRST TIME EXPERIENCING THIS

HAVING A BLAST

I GIVE THE TRIP
☆☆☆☆☆
STARS!

CAMPING TRIP 5

at _____

Dates

Overnights
1 2 3 4

Weather

Sleeping in a

I want to
remember this story

HERE'S THE SPOT

I see

I hear

I touch

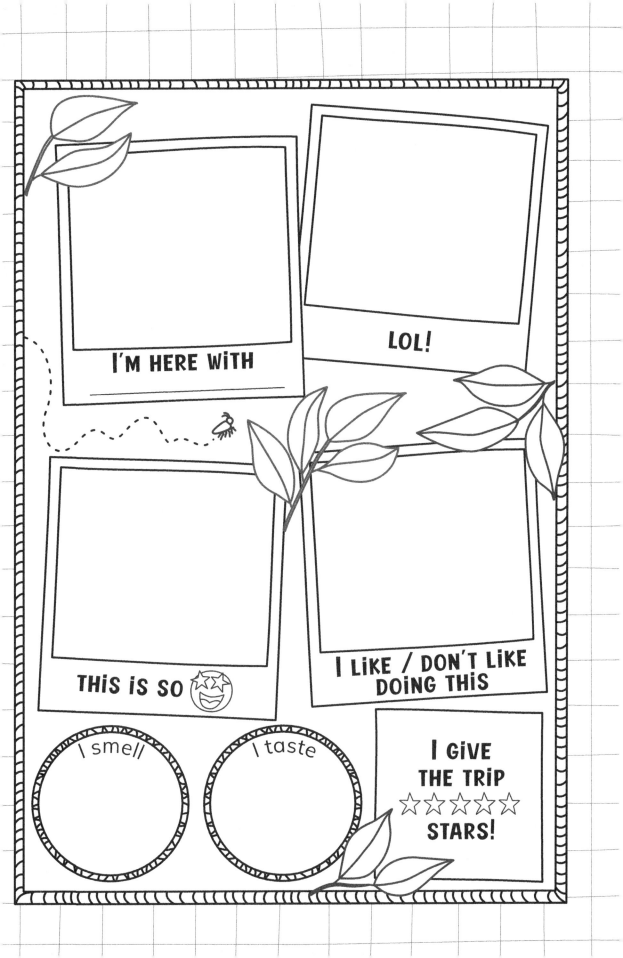

CAMPING TRIP 6

at _____

Dates

Overnights
1 2 3 4 ◊

Weather

Sleeping in a

Glad I brought

HERE'S THE SPOT

I want to remember this story

I'M HERE WITH

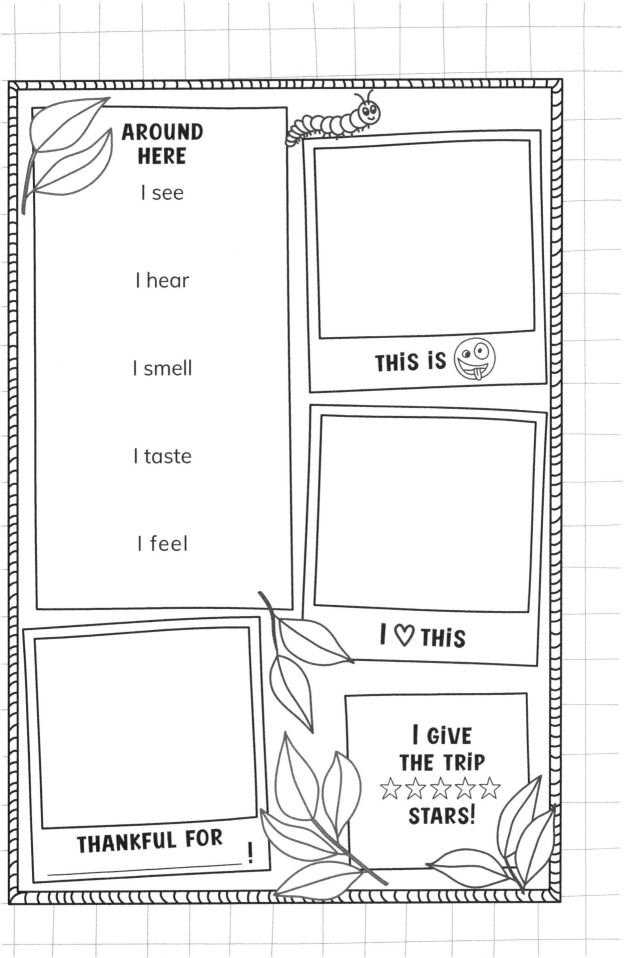

AROUND HERE

I see

I hear

I smell

I taste

I feel

THIS IS

I ♡ THIS

THANKFUL FOR
____ !

I GIVE
THE TRIP
☆☆☆☆☆
STARS!

CAMPiNG TRiP 7

at _____

Dates

Overnights
① ② ③ ④ ◇

Sleeping in a

Weather

HERE'S THE SPOT

I'M HERE WiTH

_____

I see

I hear

I taste

I smell

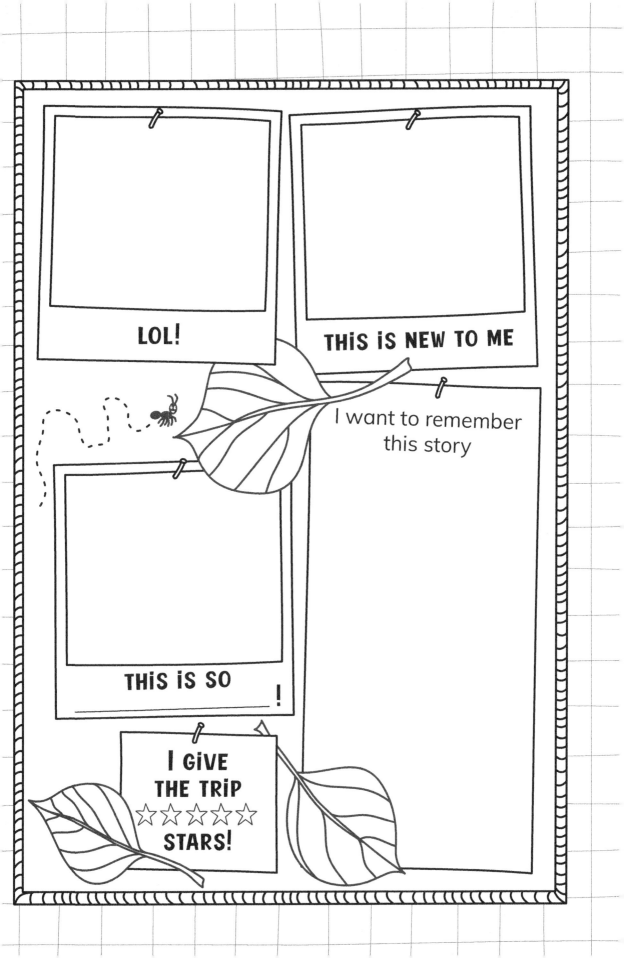

CAMPING TRIP 8

at _____

Dates

Overnights
(1)(2)(3)(4) (leaf)

Weather

Sleeping in a

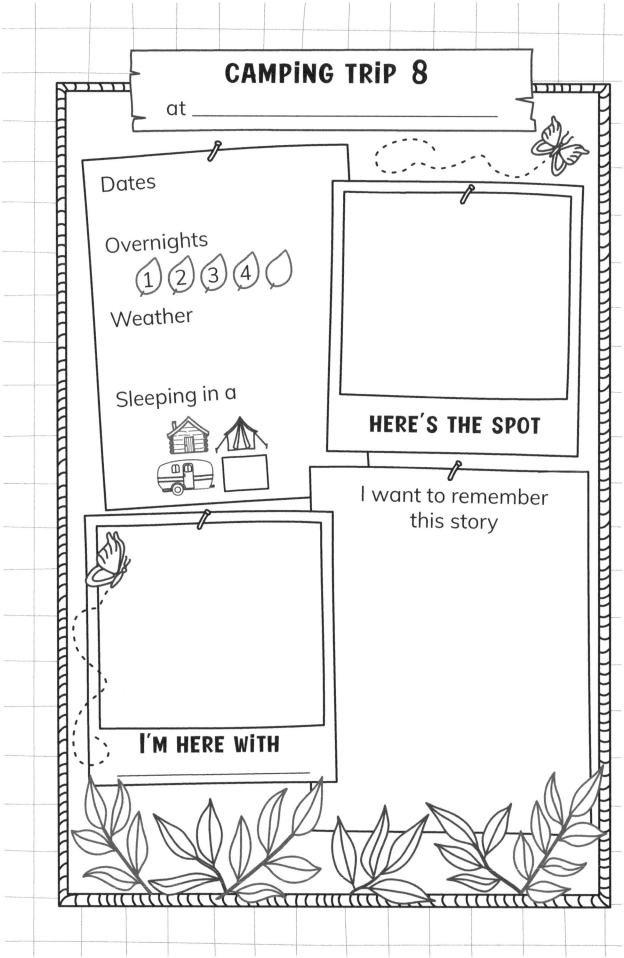

HERE'S THE SPOT

I want to remember
this story

I'M HERE WITH
_____

I see

I hear

I smell

I taste

I feel

I wonder

FIRST TIME EXPERIENCING THIS

HAVING A BLAST

I GIVE THE TRIP
☆☆☆☆☆
STARS!

CAMPING TRIP 9

at _____

Dates

Overnights
①②③④ 🍃

Weather

Sleeping in a

I want to
remember this story

HERE'S THE SPOT

I see

I hear

I touch

I'M HERE WITH

LOL!

THIS IS SO

I LIKE / DON'T LIKE DOING THIS

I smell

I taste

I GIVE THE TRIP ☆☆☆☆☆ STARS!

CAMPING TRIP 10

at _____

Dates

Overnights

1 2 3 4

Weather

Sleeping in a

Glad I brought

HERE'S THE SPOT

I want to remember this story

I'M HERE WITH

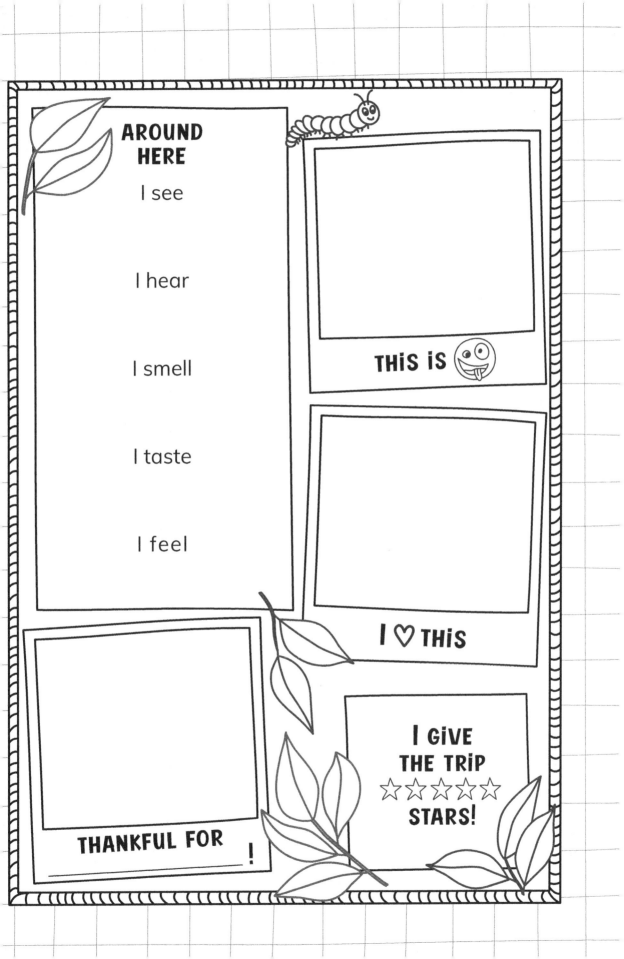

AROUND HERE

I see

I hear

I smell

I taste

I feel

THIS IS

I ♡ THIS

THANKFUL FOR _____ !

I GIVE THE TRIP ☆☆☆☆☆ STARS!

CAMPING TRIP 11

at _____

Dates

Overnights
① ② ③ ④ ⬙

Sleeping in a

Weather

I see

I hear

I taste

I smell

HERE'S THE SPOT

I'M HERE WITH
_____

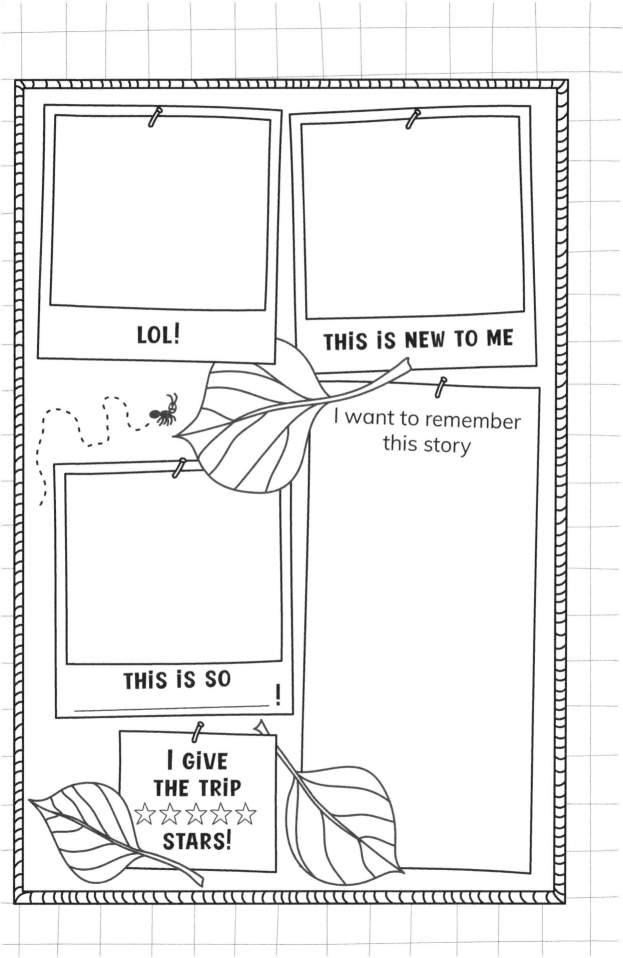

LOL!

THIS IS NEW TO ME

I want to remember this story

THIS IS SO ___ !

I GIVE THE TRIP ☆☆☆☆☆ STARS!

CAMPING TRIP 12

at _____

Dates

Overnights
(1)(2)(3)(4) leaf

Weather

Sleeping in a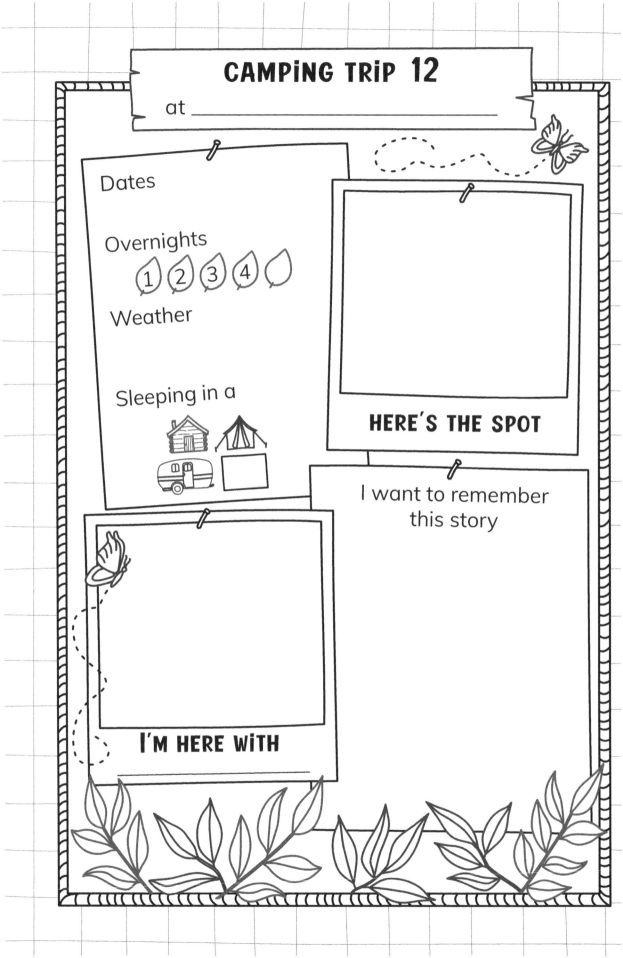

HERE'S THE SPOT

I want to remember this story

I'M HERE WITH

_____

I see

I hear

I smell

I taste

I feel

I wonder

FIRST TIME EXPERIENCING THIS

HAVING A BLAST

I GIVE THE TRIP ☆☆☆☆☆ STARS!

CAMPING TRIP 13

at _____

Dates

Overnights
1 2 3 4

Weather

Sleeping in a
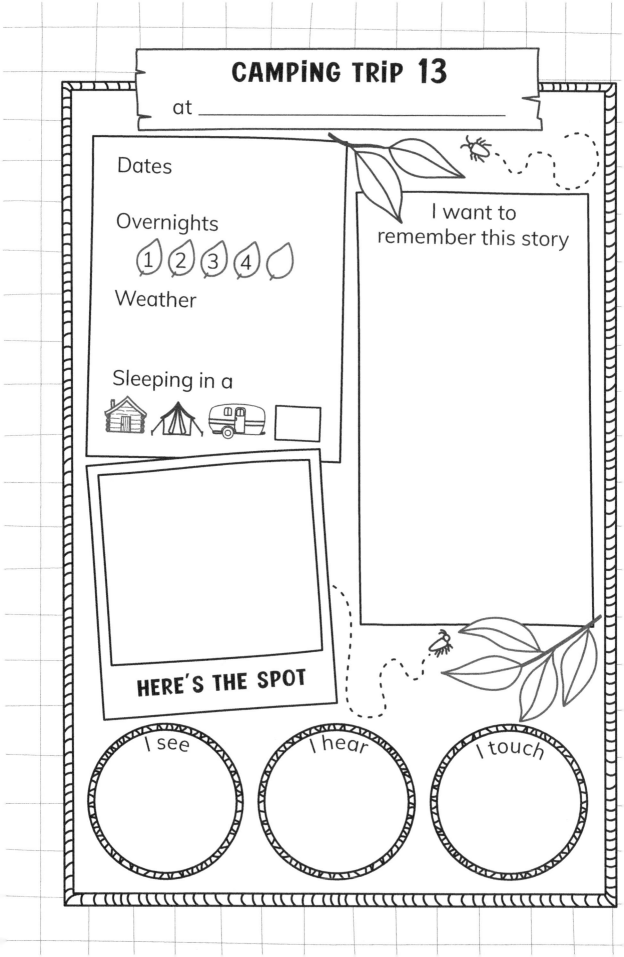

I want to remember this story

HERE'S THE SPOT

I see

I hear

I touch

I'M HERE WITH

LOL!

THIS IS SO

I LIKE / DON'T LIKE DOING THIS

I smell

I taste

I GIVE THE TRIP ☆☆☆☆☆ STARS!

CAMPING TRIP 14

at _____

Dates

Overnights
1 2 3 4

Weather

Sleeping in a

Glad I brought

HERE'S THE SPOT

I want to remember
this story

I'M HERE WITH

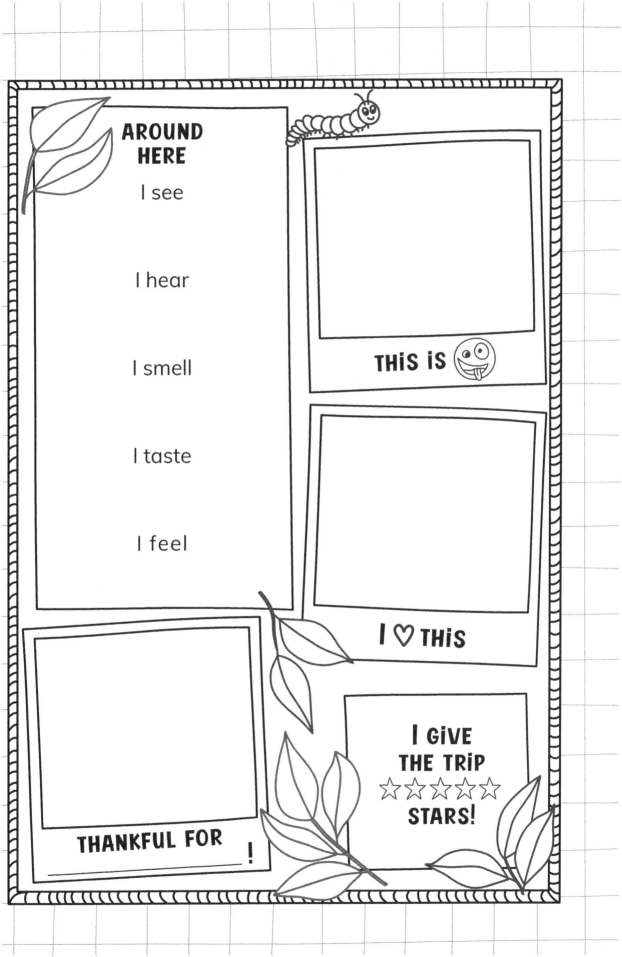

AROUND HERE

I see

I hear

I smell

I taste

I feel

THIS IS

I ♡ THIS

THANKFUL FOR ___ !

I GIVE THE TRIP ☆☆☆☆☆ STARS!

CAMPING TRIP 15

at _____

Dates

Overnights
① ② ③ ④ ⟨leaf⟩

Sleeping in a

Weather

I see

I hear

I taste

I smell

HERE'S THE SPOT

I'M HERE WITH
_____

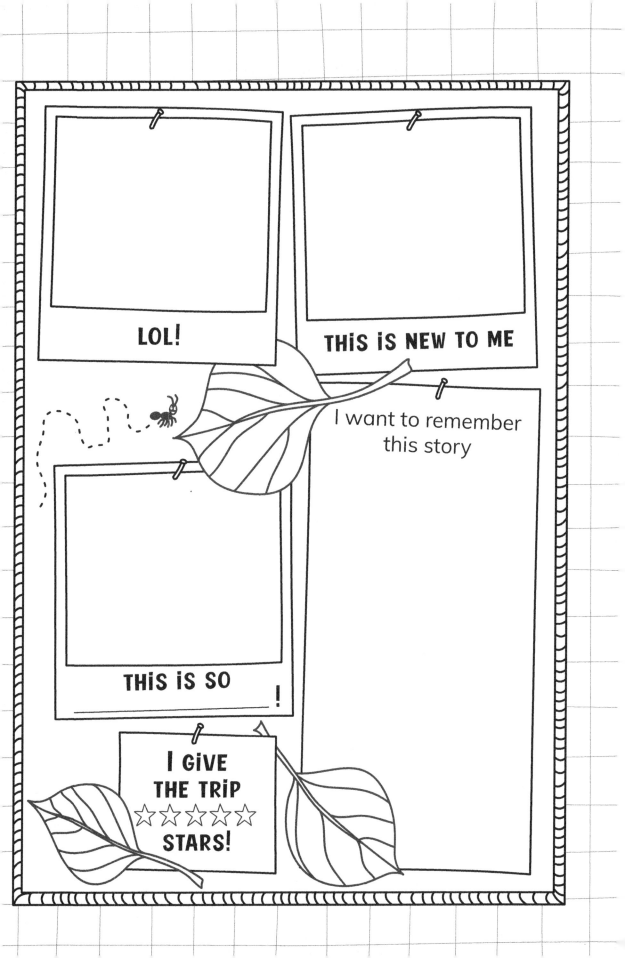

LOL!

THIS IS NEW TO ME

I want to remember this story

THIS IS SO _____ !

I GIVE THE TRIP ☆☆☆☆☆ STARS!

CAMPING TRIP 16

at _____

Dates

Overnights

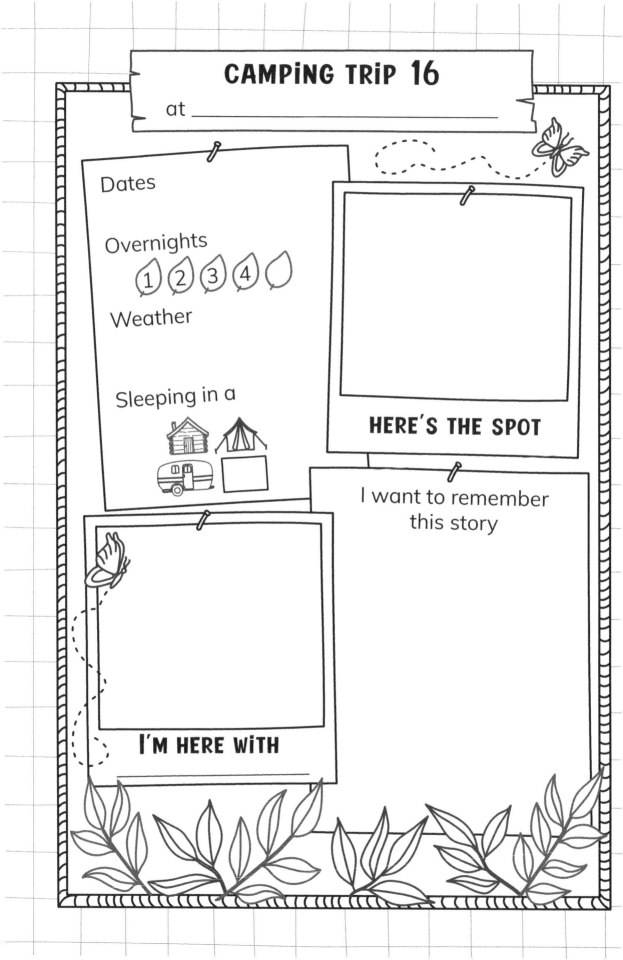

1 2 3 4

Weather

Sleeping in a

HERE'S THE SPOT

I want to remember
this story

I'M HERE WITH

I see

I hear

I smell

I taste

I feel

I wonder

FiRST TiME EXPERiENCiNG THiS

HAViNG A BLAST

I GiVE THE TRiP ☆☆☆☆☆ **STARS!**

CAMPING TRIP 17

at _____

Dates

Overnights

1 2 3 4

Weather

Sleeping in a

I want to
remember this story

HERE'S THE SPOT

I see

I hear

I touch

I'M HERE WITH

LOL!

THIS IS SO

I LIKE / DON'T LIKE DOING THIS

I smell

I taste

I GIVE THE TRIP ☆☆☆☆☆ STARS!

CAMPING TRIP 18

at _____

Dates

Overnights
1 2 3 4

Weather

Sleeping in a

Glad I brought

HERE'S THE SPOT

I want to remember
this story

I'M HERE WITH

AROUND HERE

I see

I hear

I smell

I taste

I feel

THIS IS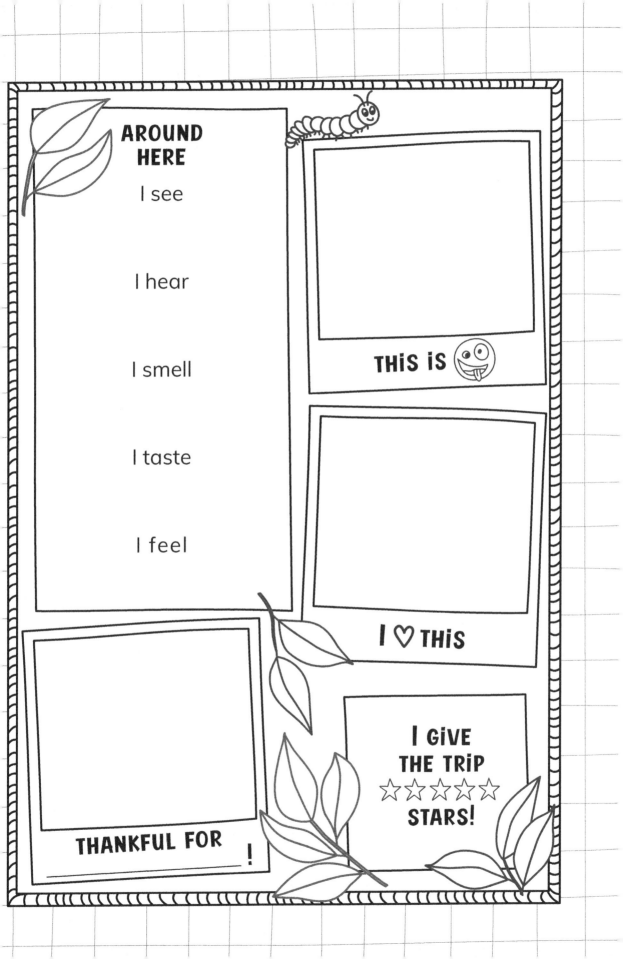

I ♡ THIS

THANKFUL FOR _____ !

I GIVE
THE TRIP
☆☆☆☆☆
STARS!

CAMPING TRIP 19

at _____

Dates

Overnights
1 2 3 4 ◇

Sleeping in a

Weather

I see

I hear

I taste

I smell

HERE'S THE SPOT

I'M HERE WITH

_____

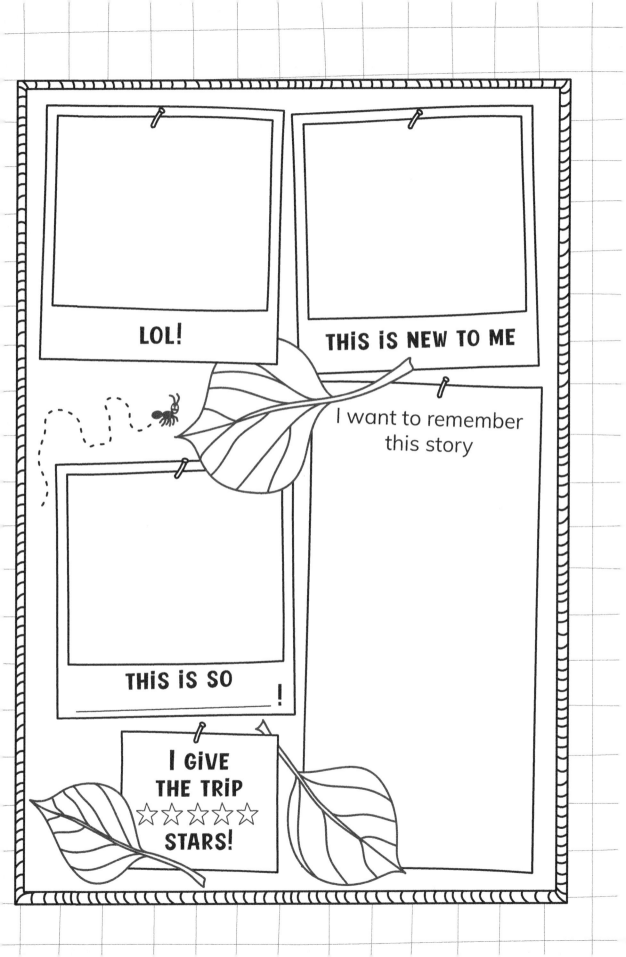

LOL!

THIS IS NEW TO ME

I want to remember this story

THIS IS SO _____ !

I GIVE
THE TRIP
☆☆☆☆☆
STARS!

CAMPING TRIP 20

at _____

Dates

Overnights
① ② ③ 4 〔leaf〕

Weather

Sleeping in a
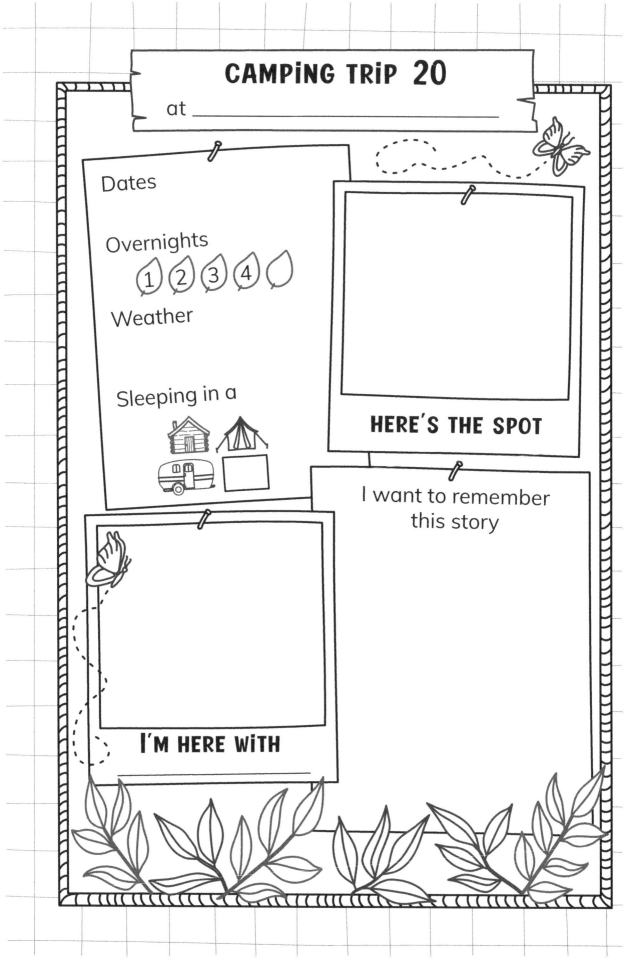

HERE'S THE SPOT

I want to remember this story

I'M HERE WITH
_____

I see

I hear

I smell

I taste

I feel

I wonder

FIRST TIME
EXPERIENCING THIS

HAVING A BLAST

I GIVE THE TRIP
☆☆☆☆☆
STARS!

CAMPING TRIP 21

at _____

Dates

Overnights
① ② ③ ④ ⑤

Weather

Sleeping in a

I want to remember this story

HERE'S THE SPOT

I see

I hear

I touch

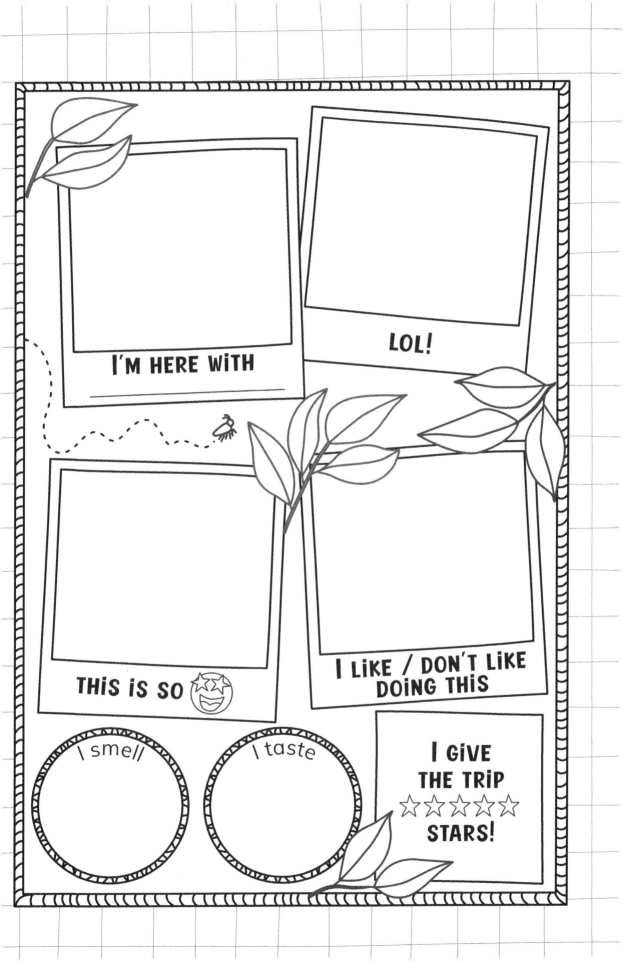

CAMPING TRIP 22

at _____

Dates

Overnights

1 2 3 4

Weather

Sleeping in a

Glad I brought

HERE'S THE SPOT

I want to remember
this story

I'M HERE WITH

AROUND HERE

I see

I hear

I smell

I taste

I feel

THIS IS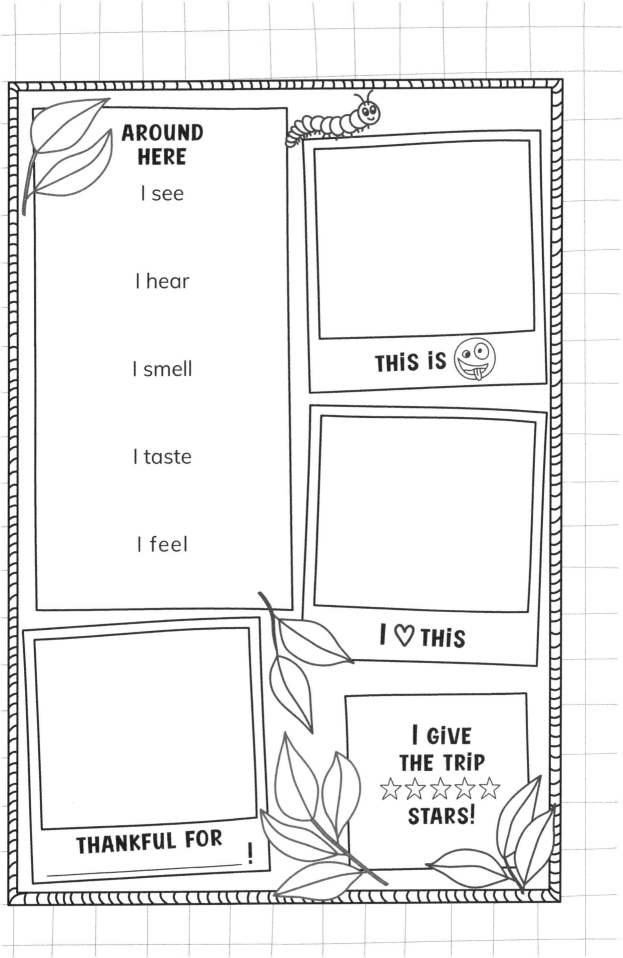

I ♡ THIS

THANKFUL FOR ____ !

I GIVE
THE TRIP
☆☆☆☆☆
STARS!

CAMPING TRIP 23

at _____

Dates

Overnights
① ② ③ ④ ⬭

Sleeping in a

Weather

I see

I hear

I taste

I smell

HERE'S THE SPOT

I'M HERE WITH
_____

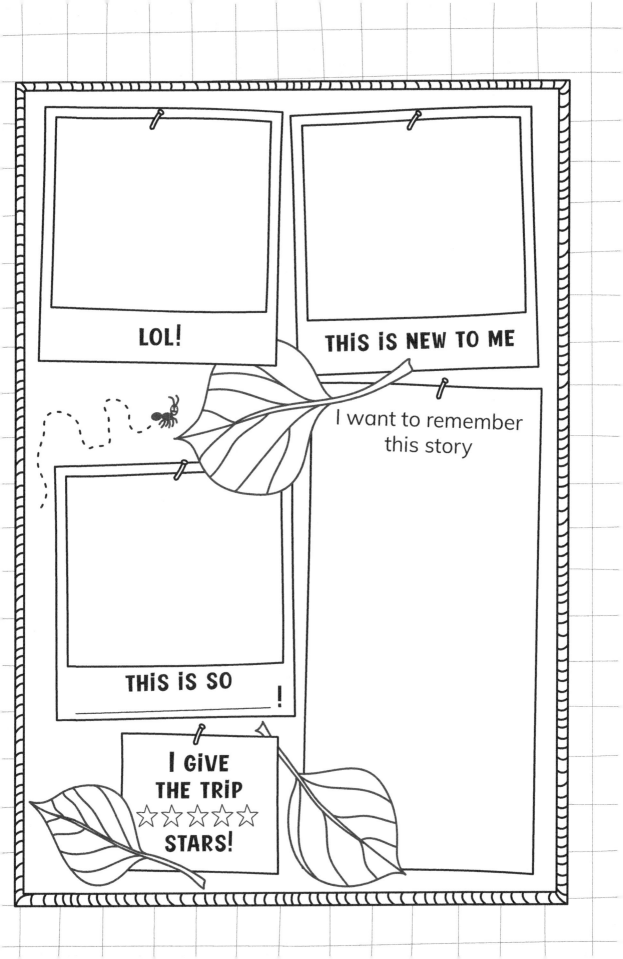

LOL!

THIS IS NEW TO ME

I want to remember this story

THIS IS SO _____ !

I GIVE THE TRIP ☆☆☆☆☆ STARS!

CAMPING TRIP 24

at _____

Dates

Overnights
1 2 3 4

Weather

Sleeping in a

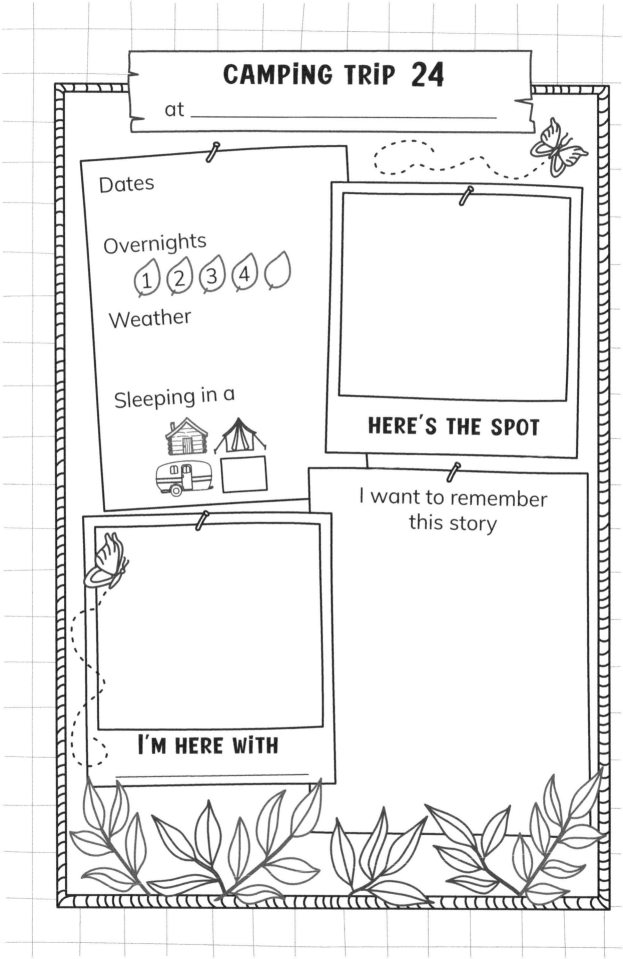

HERE'S THE SPOT

I want to remember
this story

I'M HERE WITH

I see

I hear

I smell

I taste

I feel

I wonder

FIRST TIME
EXPERIENCING THIS

HAVING A BLAST

I GIVE THE TRIP
☆☆☆☆☆
STARS!

CAMPING TRIP 25

at _____

Dates

Overnights
① ② ③ ④ (5)

Weather

Sleeping in a

I want to
remember this story

HERE'S THE SPOT

I see

I hear

I touch

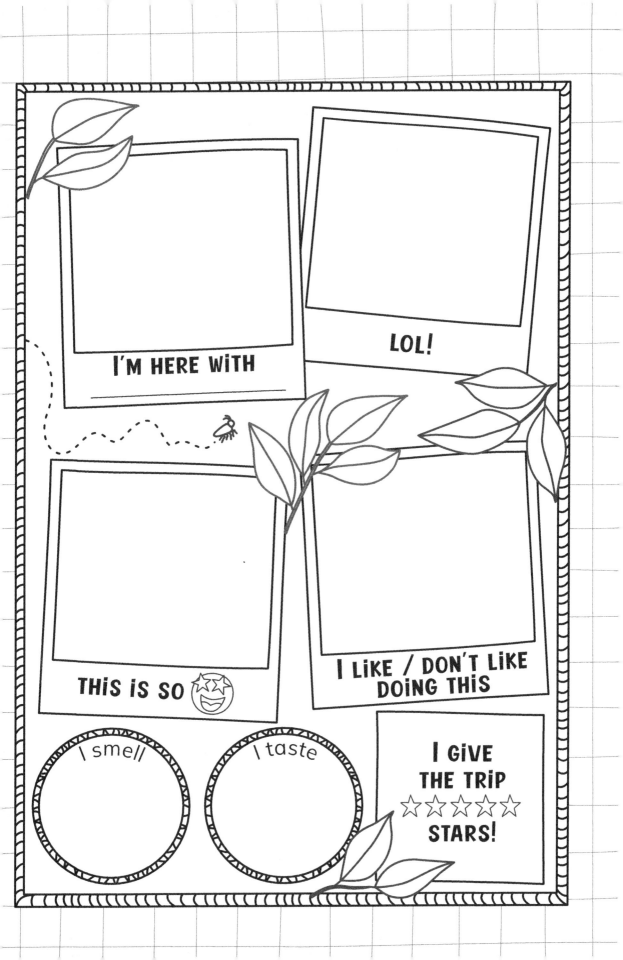

I'M HERE WITH

LOL!

THIS IS SO

I LIKE / DON'T LIKE DOING THIS

I smell

I taste

I GIVE THE TRIP ☆☆☆☆☆ STARS!

A FEW LAST
ADVENTURE NOTES
TO REMEMBER

THE END . . . ALMOST

☐ I camped 25 times!

☐ I journaled adventures.

☐ I tried to leave my campsites cleaner than I found them.

☐ I had fun!

I LOVED THIS!

☐ OKAY, NOW I'M FINISHED!

ONE LAST PICTURE OF ME

LET'S CELEBRATE MORE OF YOUR STORY!

I believe your story is one of the most meaningful gifts you can give yourself. THANK YOU for entrusting me and this journal during your camping adventures.

Let's keep collecting your stories—I call it storycatching, and we'll do it together. Join me at **katieclemons.com** to see my entire collection of books and projects. Below are a few treasures you might especially enjoy!

Katie

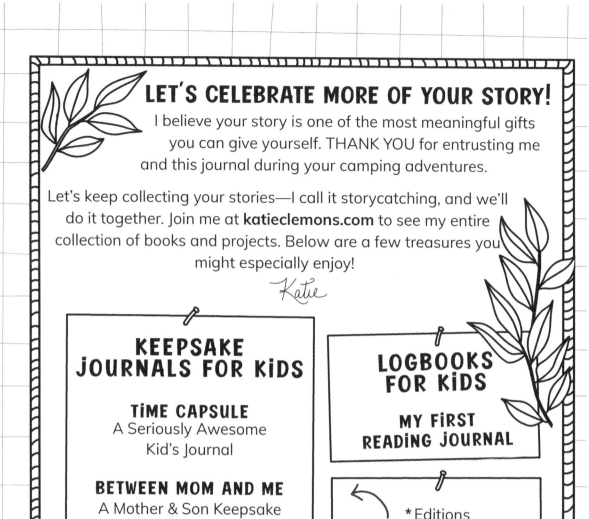

KEEPSAKE JOURNALS FOR KIDS

TIME CAPSULE
A Seriously Awesome Kid's Journal

BETWEEN MOM AND ME
A Mother & Son Keepsake Journal*

LOVE, MOM AND ME
A Mother & Daughter Keepsake Journal*

HERE I GO!
A Travel Journal

WE ARE SO THANKFUL
An Adult & Child Gratitude Journal

OUR PRAYER JOURNAL
An Adult & Child Christian Prayer Journal

LOGBOOKS FOR KIDS

MY FIRST READING JOURNAL

*Editions for **KIDS** to share with **DAD**, **GRANDMA**, and **GRANDPA** too!

Kid journals

Free printables

Nature drawing

Made in the USA
Monee, IL
14 May 2022

96367098R00057